THE BEST OF DREAMBOATS & PETTICOATS

ALL ALONE AM I 3
BRENDA LEE

ALL I HAVE TO DO IS DREAM 6
THE EVERLY BROTHERS

ARE YOU SURE? 12
THE ALLISONS

AT THE HOP 9
DANNY & THE JUNIORS

BE-BOP-A-LULA 16
GENE VINCENT & HIS BLUE CAPS

BLUE VELVET 18
BOBBY VINTON

BOBBY'S GIRL 21
SUSAN MAUGHAN

CHANTILLY LACE 24
THE BIG BOPPER

COME OUTSIDE 27
MIKE SARNE & WENDY RICHARDS

DONNA 32
MARTY WILDE

THE END OF THE WORLD 36
SKEETER DAVIS

GOOD TIMIN' 42
JIMMY JONES

GREAT BALLS OF FIRE 45
JERRY LEE LEWIS

THE GREAT PRETENDER 48
THE PLATTERS

HEARTBEAT 55
BUDDY HOLLY

IN DREAMS 62
ROY ORBISON

IN THE STILL OF THE NIGHT 58
THE FIVE SATINS

IT'S ALMOST TOMORROW 67
MARK WYNTER

IT'S NOW OR NEVER 70
ELVIS PRESLEY

JOHNNY REMEMBER ME 75
JOHN LEYTON

JUST LIKE EDDIE 80
HEINZ

LET'S TWIST AGAIN 85
CHUBBY CHECKER

LIKE I'VE NEVER BEEN GONE 90
BILLY FURY

LIPSTICK ON YOUR COLLAR 94
CONNIE FRANCIS

MOVE OVER DARLING 97
DORIS DAY

ONLY THE LONELY 102
ROY ORBISON

ROCK AROUND THE CLOCK 104
BILL HALEY & HIS COMETS

ROCK ISLAND LINE 106
LONNIE DONEGAN & HIS SKIFFLE GROUP

RUBBER BALL 113
BOBBY VEE

RUNAROUND SUE 118
DION

RUNAWAY 122
DEL SHANNON

SHEILA 130
TOMMY ROE

SINGING THE BLUES 127
TOMMY STEELE

SMOKE GETS IN YOUR EYES 134
THE PLATTERS

A TEENAGER IN LOVE 140
MARTY WILDE

TELSTAR 144
THE TORNADOS

THAT'S WHAT LOVE WILL DO 148
JOE BROWN & THE BRUVVERS

WAKE UP LITTLE SUSIE 152
THE EVERLY BROTHERS

WALKIN' BACK TO HAPPINESS 156
HELEN SHAPIRO

WELL I ASK YOU 162
EDEN KANE

WHEN 166
THE KALIN TWINS

**A WHITE SPORT COAT
(AND A PINK CARNATION)** 137
TERRY DENE

YOU NEVER CAN TELL 174
CHUCK BERRY

YOUNG LOVE 172
TAB HUNTER

WISE PUBLICATIONS
PART OF THE MUSIC SALES GROUP
LONDON / NEW YORK / PARIS / SYDNEY / COPENHAGEN / BERLIN / MADRID / TOKYO

Published by

Wise Publications
14-15 Berners Street, London W1T 3LJ, UK

Exclusive Distributors:

Music Sales Limited
Distribution Centre, Newmarket Road,
Bury St Edmunds, Suffolk IP33 3YB, UK

Music Sales Pty Limited
20 Resolution Drive,
Caringbah, NSW 2229, Australia

Order No. AM998987
ISBN 978-1-84938-304-2
This book © Copyright 2009 Wise Publications,
a division of Music Sales Limited.

Edited by Jenni Wheeler.
Music processed by Paul Ewers Music Design.

Printed in the EU

www.musicsales.com

Your Guarantee of Quality
As publishers, we strive to produce every book
to the highest commercial standards.
The music has been freshly engraved and the book has
been carefully designed to minimise awkward page turns
and to make playing from it a real pleasure.
Particular care has been given to specifying acid-free,
neutral-sized paper made from pulps which have not been
elemental chlorine bleached. This pulp is from farmed
sustainable forests and was produced with special regard
for the environment.
Throughout, the printing and binding have been planned
to ensure a sturdy, attractive publication which should
give years of enjoyment.
If your copy fails to meet our high standards,
please inform us and we will gladly replace it.

ALL ALONE AM I

Music by Manos Hadjidakis
Words by Ioannis Ioannidis
English Translation by Arthur Altman

4

ALL I HAVE TO DO IS DREAM

Words & Music by Boudleaux Bryant

-ev-er I want you__ all I have to do is dream,_____ dream, dream, dream. 2. When

-ev-er I want you__ all I have to do is

dream._____

I can make you mine,

taste your lips of wine, an-y-time, night or day.

On-ly trou-ble is, gee whiz, I'm dream-ing my life__ a-

7

-way!_____ I need you so that I could die, I love you so

and that is why when-ev-er I want you___ all I have to do is

dream._____ dream._____

Dream, dream, dream,_ dream,_____ dream, dream, dream,_ dream.

AT THE HOP

Words & Music by Arthur Singer, John Medora & David White

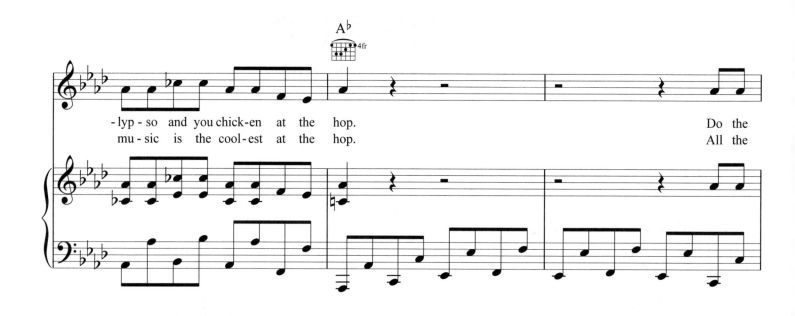

-lyp - so and you chick-en at the hop.
mu - sic is the cool-est at the hop.

Do the
All the

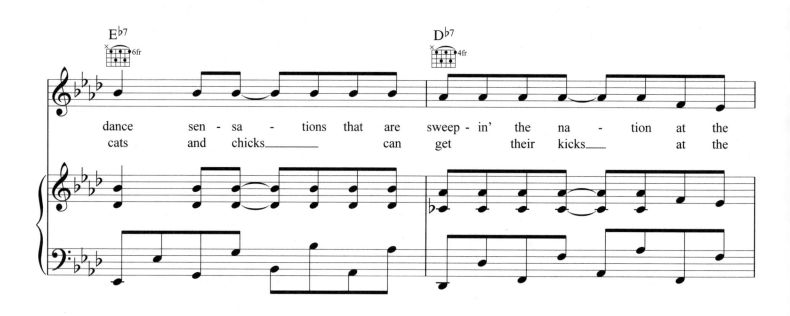

dance sen - sa - tions that are sweep-in' the na - tion at the
cats and chicks_____ can get their kicks____ at the

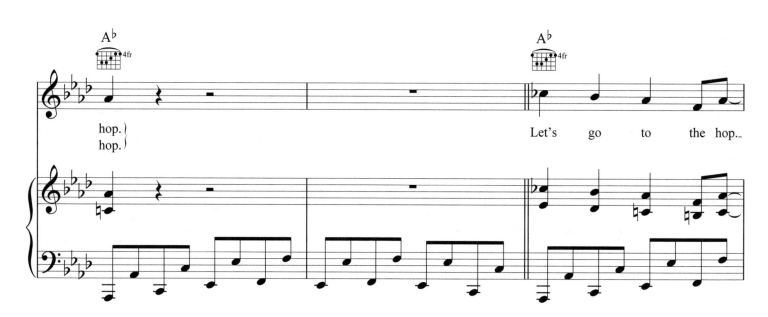

hop.
hop.

Let's go to the hop._

Lyrics (vocal line):

(Oh ba - by.) Let's go to the hop.___ (Oh ba - by.)

Let's go to the hop.___ (Oh ba - by.) Let's go to the hop.___

___ (Oh ba - by.) Come on,

let's go to the hop.___ 2. Oh you can

ARE YOU SURE

Words & Music by John Allison

Are you sure_ you won't be sor - ry? Comes to-mor-row you won't want_ me

back a-gain_ to hold you tight - ly._____ 1. Now
2. Just

are you sure it's not your fool-ish heart,_ that
stop and think, it's your de-ci-sion now,_ for

you won't grieve if we're to be a-part?_
you're the one who went and broke the vow._

BE-BOP-A-LULA

Words & Music by Gene Vincent & Sheriff Tex Davis

16

BLUE VELVET

Words & Music by Bernie Wayne & Lee Morris

blue vel - vet, blu - er than vel - vet were her eyes,

warm - er than May her ten - der sighs, love was ours.

Ours, a love I held tight - ly,

feel - ing the rap - ture grow, like a flame burn - ing bright - ly,

BOBBY'S GIRL

Words & Music by Henry Hoffman & Gary Klein

I know just what to say,___ I an-swer
Still in my what heart I pray,___ there soon will

right a-way.___ There's just one thing I've been___ wish-ing for.
come a day___ when I will have him all___ to my-self.

I wan-na be___ Bob-by's girl,___

___ I wan-na be___ Bob-by's girl.___

That's the most ___ im - por - tant thing ___ to me. ___

___ And if ___ I was ___ Bob - by's girl; ___ if ___ I was ___

___ Bob - by's girl, ___ what a faith - ful,

thank - ful girl I'd be. ___

CHANTILLY LACE

Words & Music by J.P. Richardson

(Spoken ad lib.) Hello baby, yeah, this is the Big Bopper speaking.
Oh you sweet thing.
Do I what?
Will I what?
Oh, baby, you know what I like...

Moderate boogie woogie

arp. ad lib.

Chan-til - ly lace__ __ and a pret-ty face__ and a po-ny tail__ hang in' down,__ a wig-gle in her walk and a gig-gle in her talk, they're gon-na make the world go 'round.__ Ain't

25

Verse 3: (patter)
Woo ha ha ha ha ha honey, you're tearin' me up on this telephone.
I swear I don't know what I'm gonna do with you, you yap yap and yap
and yap and yap and yap but when you break it all down you know
what I like.

Chantilly lace ...

COME OUTSIDE

Words & Music by Chris Blackwell

'cause it ain't right to want to keep on danc - ing,_____ there won't be an - y time left for ro - manc - ing. Come out - side,____ come out - side, there's a love - ly moon up

come out-side, there's a love-ly moon up

there. Come out-side,

come out-side, while we've got time to

spare 3. Lit - tle

D.S. al Coda Coda

DONNA

Words & Music by Ritchie Valens

THE END OF THE WORLD

Words by Sylvia Dee
Music by Arthur Kent

Don't they___ know___ it's the end___ of the world, 'cause

you don't love me___ an - y - more?

2. Why___ do the birds___ go on sing - ing?___

wake up in the morn - ing and I won - der_____ why

ev-'ry-thing's_ the same___ as it was. I can't un - der - stand,__ no I

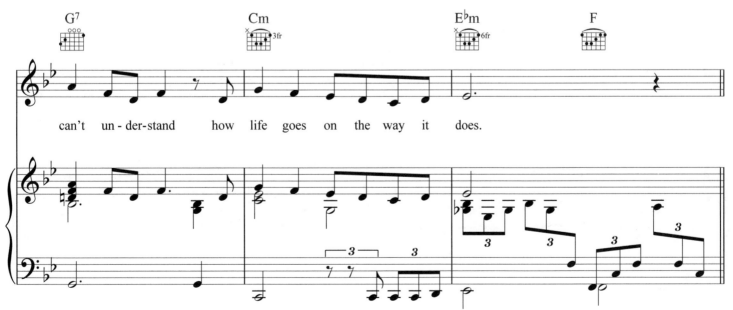

can't un - der-stand how life goes on the way it does.

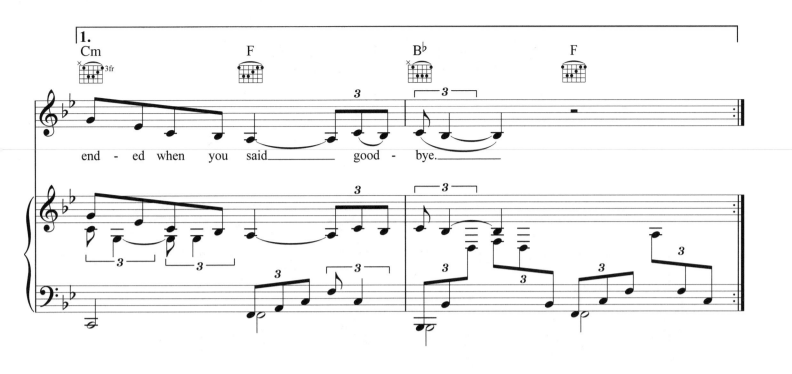

end - ed when you said_____ good - bye._____

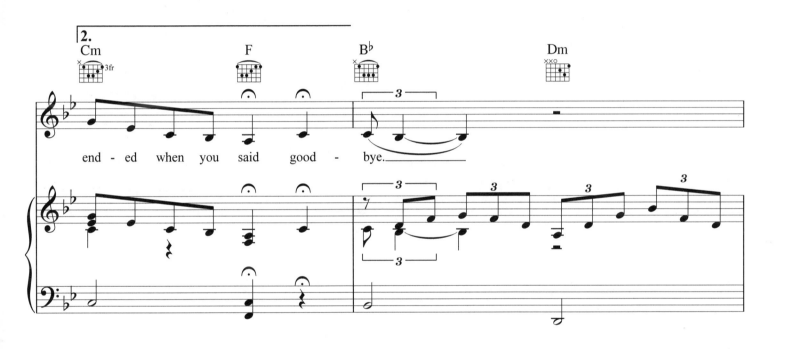

end - ed when you said good - bye._____

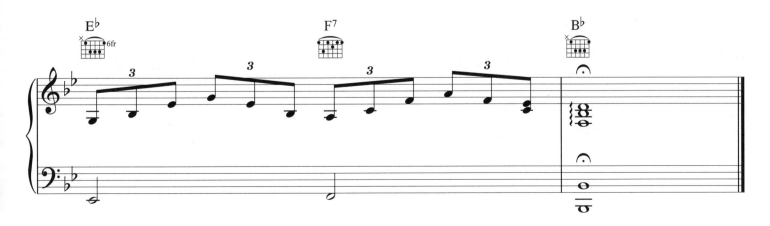

GOOD TIMIN'

Words & Music by Clint Ballard & Frederick Tobias

GREAT BALLS OF FIRE

Words & Music by Otis Blackwell & Jack Hammer

THE GREAT PRETENDER

Words & Music by Buck Ram

clown.___ I_____ seem_____ to be what I'm not, you_____ see._____ I'm wear - ing_____ my heart like a crown. Pre - -tend - ing that you're, pre - tend - ing that

53

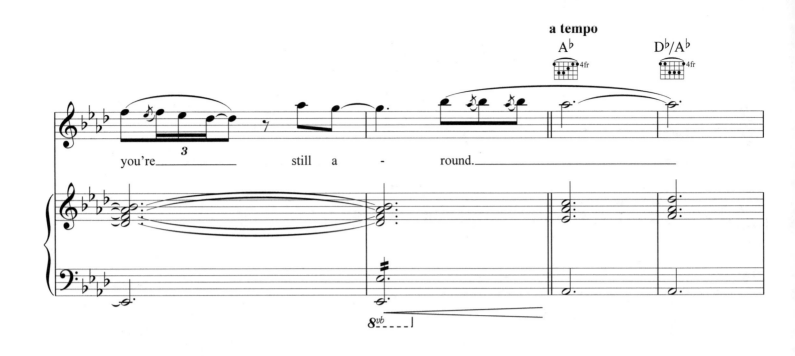

you're_____ still a - round._____

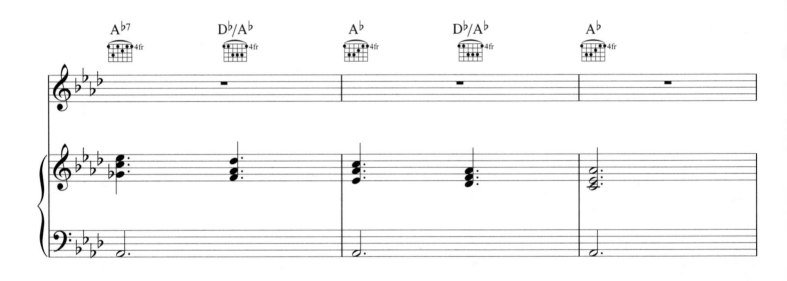

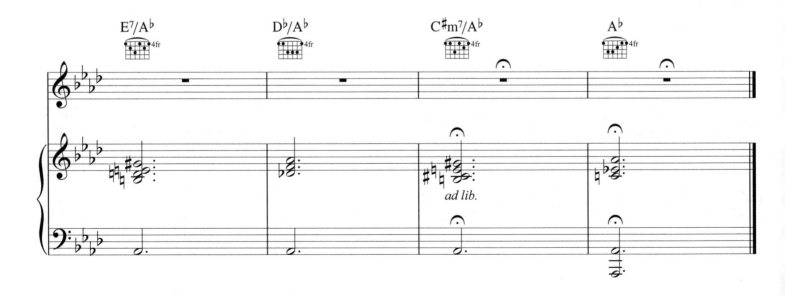

HEARTBEAT

Words & Music by Bob Montgomery & Norman Petty

Heart - beat,__ why does a love kiss__ stay in my mem - o -
Heart - beat,__ why do you love flip then__ give me a skip beat

- ry?
sign?

Rid - dl - y- pat,__ I know that new__ love thrills__ me.
Rid - dl - y- pat,__ and sing to me__ love's sto - ry.__

I know that true__ love, will__ me._____
And bring to me__ love's glo - ry._____

Heart - beat,___ why do you miss when___ my ba - by kiss - es me?

IN THE STILL OF THE NIGHT

Words & Music by Frederick Parris

IN DREAMS

Words & Music by Roy Orbison

IT'S ALMOST TOMORROW

Words & Music by Wade Buff & Gene Adkinson

IT'S NOW OR NEVER

Words & Music by Wally Gold, Aaron Schroeder & Eduardo Di Capua

tight.   Kiss me my dar - ling,   be mine to-

- night.   To - mor - row___ will be too

late;   it's now or nev - er,   my love won't

wait.   2. Just like a   It's now or nev - er,

Verse 2:
Just like a willow, we would cry an ocean
If we lost true love and sweet devotion.
Your lips excite me, let your arms invite me
For who knows when we'll meet again this way?

JOHNNY REMEMBER ME

Words & Music by Geoffrey Goddard

JUST LIKE EDDIE

Words & Music by Geoffrey Goddard

LET'S TWIST AGAIN

Words & Music by Kal Mann & Dave Appell

twist a-gain like we did last sum-mer. Yeah,____ let's
(2.) twist a-gain like we did last sum-mer. Come on let's

twist a-gain like we did last____ year.__ Do you re-
twist a-gain like we did last____ year.__ Do you re-

-mem-ber when things were real-ly hum-min'? Yeah,____ let's
-mem-ber when things were real-ly hum-min'? Come on let's

twist a-gain, twist-in' time is here. Eeh!)
twist a-gain, twist-in' time is here. Eeh!) A-

year.

Twist! *Yo!*

Drums

Drums

Spoken: Who's that fly - ing up there? *Is it a bird?*

89

LIKE I'VE NEVER BEEN GONE

Words & Music by Paul Hampton & Camille Monte

1. Don't give your love to some-one while I'm a-way.
2. I'll feel your ten-der kiss-es be-fore I go to sleep.

I want you to think a-bout me each night and day.
I'll feel your arms a-round me. Just prom-ise

93

LIPSTICK ON YOUR COLLAR

Words by Edna Lewis
Music by George Goehring

Moderate rock beat

1. When you left me all a-lone___ at the Re - cord
2. You said it be - longed to me;___ made me stop and

Hop.___ Told me you were go - in' out___ for a so - da
think,___ Then I no - ticed yours was red,___ mine was ba - by

96

MOVE OVER DARLING

Words & Music by Joe Lubin, Hal Kanter & Terry Melcher

free._____ Make love to me. (The way you sigh has me wav-ing my con-science good-bye.) You can call me a fick-le thing, but I'm prac-tic-'lly yours for-ev-er be-cause...___ I yearn to be kissed. (Move o-ver darl-ing.) How

ONLY THE LONELY

Words & Music by Roy Orbison & Joe Melson

ROCK AROUND THE CLOCK

Words & Music by Max C. Freedman & Jimmy De Knight

(Verse 2 -5 see block lyric)

Verse 2:
When the clock strikes two and three and four
If the band slows down we'll yell for more.
We're gonna rock around the clock tonight
We're gonna rock, rock, rock 'til broad daylight
We're gonna rock, gonna rock around the clock tonight.

Verse 4:
When it's eight, nine, ten, eleven, too
I'll be goin' strong and so will you.
We're gonna rock around the clock tonight
We're gonna rock, rock, rock 'til broad daylight
We're gonna rock, gonna rock around the clock tonight.

Verse 3:
When the chimes ring five and six and seven
We'll be rockin' up in seventh heav'n.
We're gonna rock around the clock tonight
We're gonna rock, rock, rock 'til broad daylight
We're gonna rock, gonna rock around the clock tonight.

Verse 5:
When the clock strikes twelve, we'll cool off, then
Start a rockin' 'round the clock again.
We're gonna rock around the clock tonight
We're gonna rock, rock, rock 'til broad daylight
We're gonna rock, gonna rock around the clock tonight.

ROCK ISLAND LINE

Words & Music by Lonnie Donegan

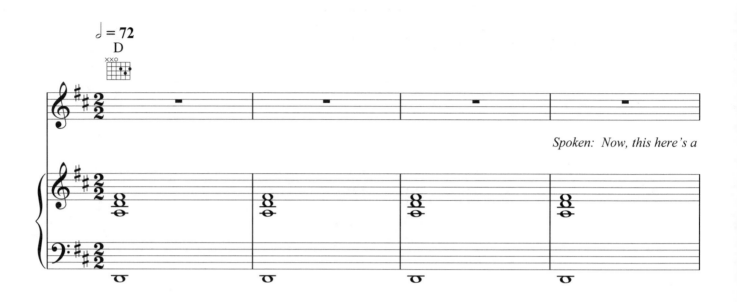

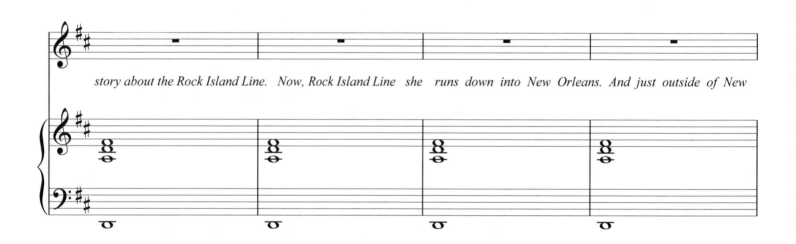

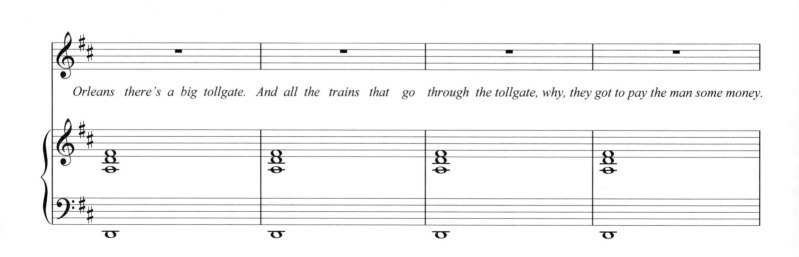

But of course, if you've got certain things on board, you're O.K. You don't have to pay the man nothin'.

And just now we see a train, she's coming down the line. And when she came up near the tollgate, the driver, he shout down to the

man. He say... I got pigs, I got hor - ses, I got

cows, I got sheep. I got all___ live - stock, I got all___

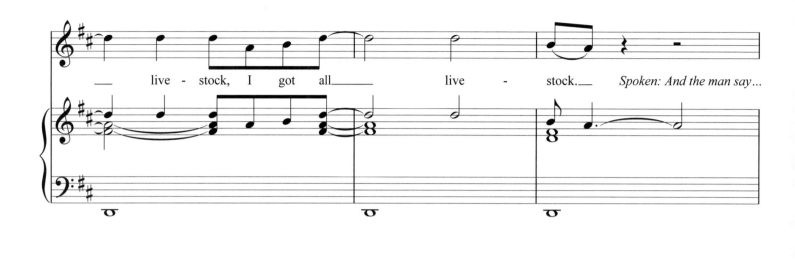

live - stock, I got all___ live - stock.___ *Spoken: And the man say...*

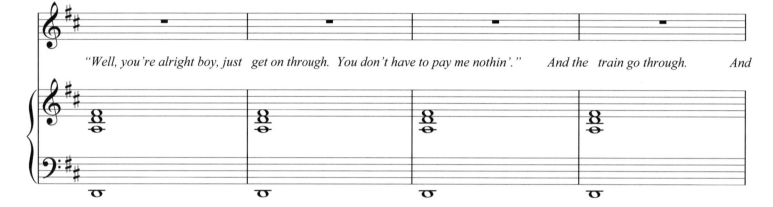

"Well, you're alright boy, just get on through. You don't have to pay me nothin'." And the train go through. And

accel.

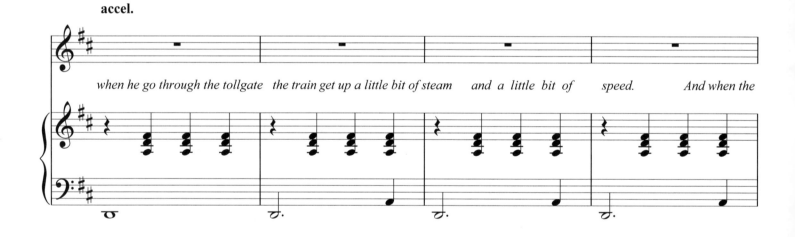

when he go through the tollgate the train get up a little bit of steam and a little bit of speed. And when the

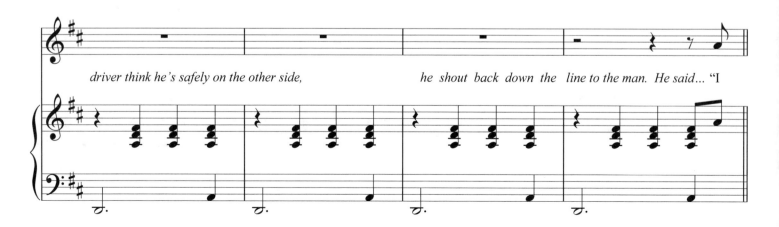

driver think he's safely on the other side, he shout back down the line to the man. He said... "I

2.

Hal - le - lu - jah, I'm safe from sin.___ The Good Lord's com-in' for to see me a-gain.___ Down the

3.

A B C dou-ble-U X Y Z. Cat's in the cup-board but he don't see me.___ Down the

D.S. al Coda

111

RUBBER BALL

Words & Music by Aaron Schroeder & Anne Orlowski

Just a rub-ber ball, 'cause you think you can be true to
Just a rub-ber band, be-cause my heart strings they just

two.__ You bounce__ my
snap.__ You go and squeeze__ me 'til I'm

heart a - round. (You don't e - ven put her down.)__ And like a
all a - flame. (She called you by some oth-er guy's__ name.) And like a

To Coda ⊕

rub-ber ball I come bounc - ing back to you. Rub-ber ball I'll come bounc - ing back to
rub-ber ball I come bounc - ing back to you. Rub-ber ball I'll come bounc - ing back to

116

RUNAROUND SUE

Words & Music by Ernie Maresca & Dion Di Mucci

hayp   hayp   bum-da ha-dy ha-dy hayp.

hayp.   Ah.

1. I should have known it from the
2. I miss her lips   and the

ver - y start,___   this girl will leave me with a bro - ken   heart.___
smile on her face,___   touch of her hair___   and this girl's warm em-brace.___

Now lis-ten peo - ple what I'm tell-ing you___ }
So if you don't wan - na cry___ like I do }

a-keep a-way from a - run a-round Sue.

119

RUNAWAY

Words & Music by Del Shannon & Max Crook

won - der where she will stay,_____

my lit - tle run-a-way._ A - run run run___ run run

run-a - way._

Organ 8va

125

126

SINGING THE BLUES

Words & Music by Melvin Endsley

SHEILA

Words & Music by Tommy Roe

SMOKE GETS IN YOUR EYES

Words by Otto Harbach
Music by Jerome Kern

They said some-day you'll find, all who love are blind._____ When your heart's on

fire, you must re-al - ize smoke gets in your eyes._____

So I chaffed them and I gay-ly laughed to think they could doubt my love.

A WHITE SPORT COAT AND A PINK CARNATION

Words & Music by Marty Robbins

someone else will hold my dreams, a white sport coat and a pink carnation, I'm in a blue, blue mood. A mood.

139

A TEENAGER IN LOVE

Words & Music by Doc Pomus & Mort Shuman

Verse 2:
One day I feel so happy
Next day I feel so sad.
I guess I'll learn to take
The good with the bad.

Each night I ask the stars above
Why must I be a teenager in love?

TELSTAR

Music by Joe Meek

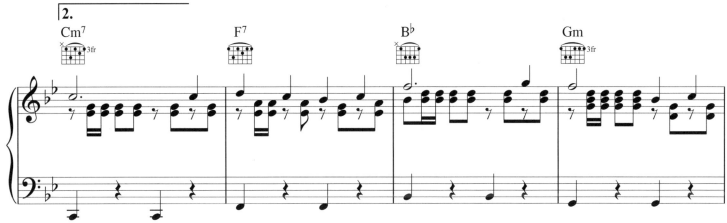

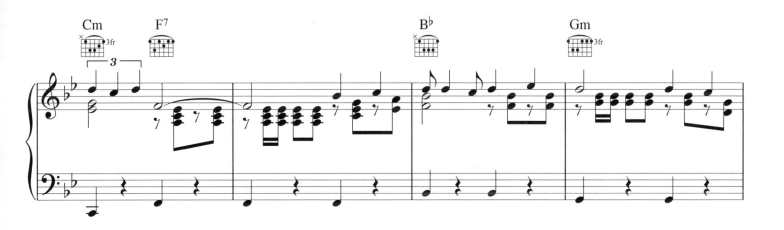

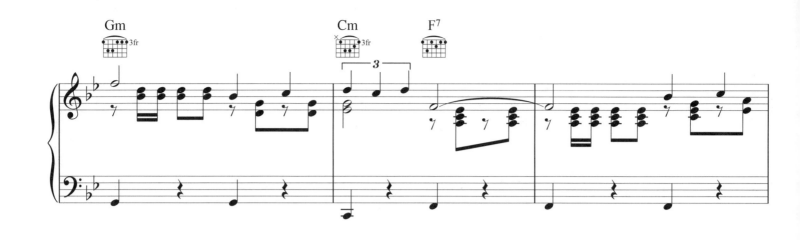

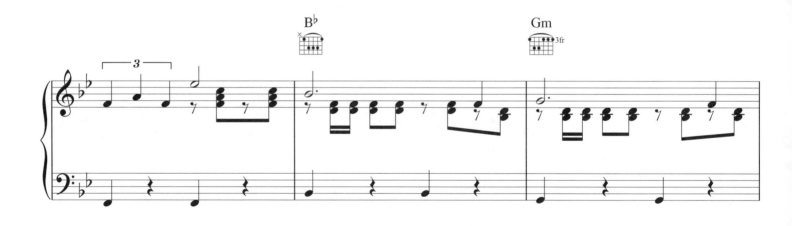

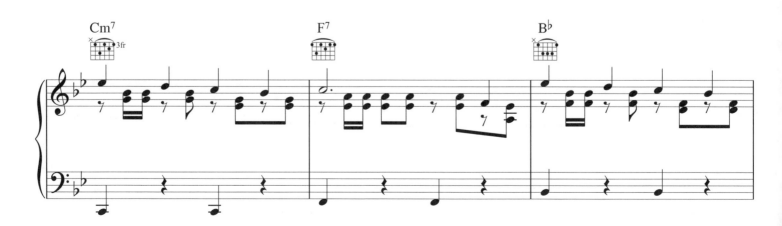

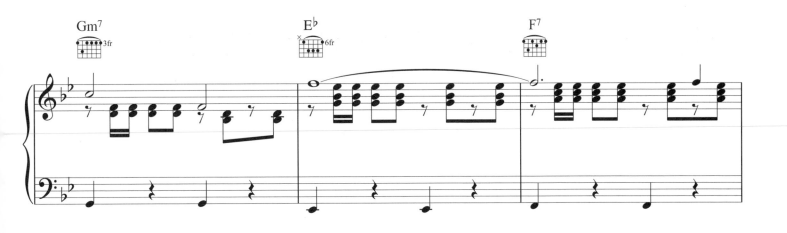

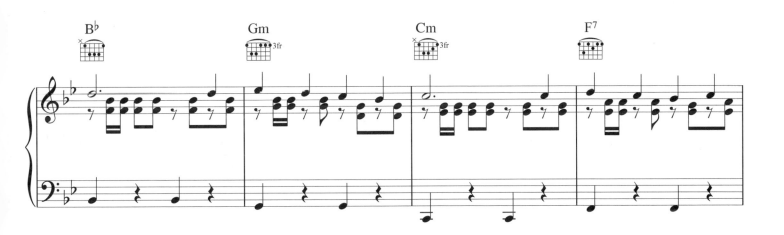

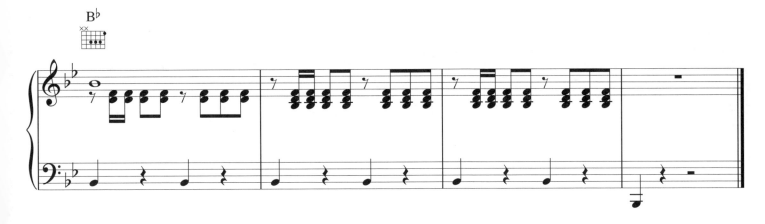

THAT'S WHAT LOVE WILL DO

Words & Music by Trevor Peacock

long - ing starts all o -ver a - gain._____
O - ver a - gain._____
O - ver a - gain.__

3. Put out__ the can - dle and to - mor-row it__ burns bright a - gain.__
4. *Instrumental till* *
5. That yel - low dress you wore when we went dan - cing Sun - day nights,__

But when I lost you it could nev - er be__ put right a - gain.__ What
* I've
(5.) that smile you give me in the mo - vies when they dim the lights,__ I've

Drums

150

WAKE UP LITTLE SUSIE

Words & Music by Felice Bryant & Boudleaux Bryant

Su - sie, ba - by, looks like we goofed a - gain._____ Wake up,___ Lit - tle

Su - sie.___ Wake up,___ Lit - tle Su - sie.___ We've got - ta go

home.

D.S. al Coda
(with repeat)

Coda

Su - sie._____

155

WALKIN' BACK TO HAPPINESS

Words & Music by John Schroeder & Mike Hawker

(Ba ba___ ba da.) Laid a - side_____ fool - ish pride,_____

learned the truth from tears I cried._____

To Coda ⊕   N.C.

D.S. al Coda   ⊕ **Coda**   N.C.

Spread the news I'm on my way._____ Whoo - pa, oh

WELL I ASK YOU

Words & Music by Johnnie Worth

now. Just you__ ask me.__

Get down on your__ knees and try. I won't__ break 'til I

see you cry__ like me when I asked you.__

Repeat to fade

Well, I ask you.__ Well, I ask you.__

WHEN

Words & Music by Paul Evans & Jack Reardon

When, when you smile,_ when you smile_ at me.

YOUNG LOVE

Words & Music by Carol Joyner & Ric Cartey

YOU NEVER CAN TELL

Words & Music by Chuck Berry

(Verses 2 - 7 see block lyric)

teen - age wed - ding and the old folks wished 'em well.

You could see that Pi - erre did tru -

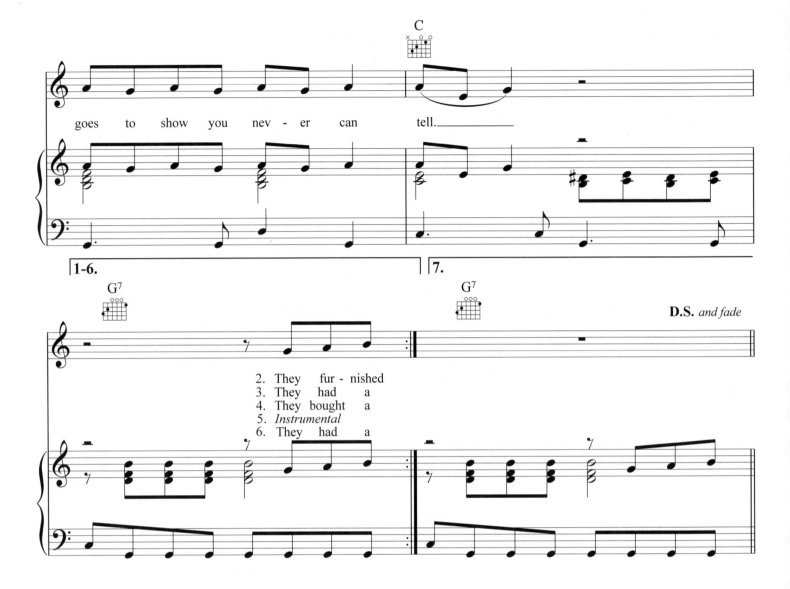

Verse 2:
They furnished off an apartment with a two-room Roebuck sale.
The Coolerator was crammed with TV dinners and ginger ale.
But when Pierre found work, the little money comin' worked out well.
C'est la vie, say the old folks, it goes to show you never can tell.

Verse 3:
They had a hi-fi phono, boy did they let it blast.
Seven hundred little records all rock, rhythm and jazz.
But when the sun went down the rapid tempo of the music fell.
C'est la vie, say the old folks, it goes to show you never can tell.

Verse 4:
They bought a souped-up jitney was a cherry-red '53.
And drove it down to Orleans to celebrate their anniversary.
It was there where Pierre was wedded to the lovely Madamoiselle.
C'est la vie, say the old folks, it goes to show you never can tell.

Verse 5:
Instrumental

Verse 6:
They had a teenage wedding and the old folks wished them well.
You could see that Pierre did truly love the Madamoiselle.
And now the young Monsieur and Madame have rung the chapel bell.
C'est la vie, say the old folks, it goes to show you never can tell.

Verse 7:
Instrumental to fade

1 2 3 4 5 6 7 8 9